BIBLE STORIES

NOAH'S ARK

Published by

Rewritten by May Kerr
Music composed and performed by Nick Cartledge • Nar

First published in 2007 © BK BOOKS 2007

ISBN: 978-1-906068-73-8

D1266795

In the beginning, there was love and peace in every corner of the world. Then, Adam and Eve disobeyed God and were banished from the Garden of Eden. Soon, their children also started disobeying God.

As time went by, wickedness and selfishness prevailed over all. God saw what a terrible place the world had become. People were lying, cheating, and killing. He realized that no one cared about being righteous, or God-fearing. Gradually, the world became a place filled with evil. Bloodshed, horrible wars, and looting had taken the place of peace and love.

Seeing all this, God's heart was filled with sorrow.

"Man has become so sinful. I feel sorry that I ever created him!"

Feeling dejected, He decided to put an end to all the evil and wickedness prevailing on the earth.

"I will destroy all men, all animals and birds on the earth, and create a whole new world!"

However, there was one good man whom God didn't want to destroy. His name was Noah.

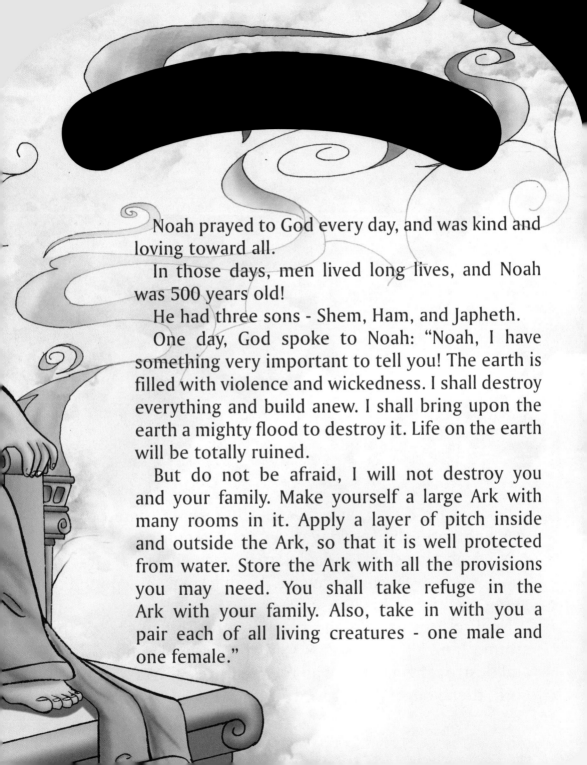

Noah prayed to God every day, and was kind and loving toward all.

In those days, men lived long lives, and Noah was 500 years old!

He had three sons - Shem, Ham, and Japheth.

One day, God spoke to Noah: "Noah, I have something very important to tell you! The earth is filled with violence and wickedness. I shall destroy everything and build anew. I shall bring upon the earth a mighty flood to destroy it. Life on the earth will be totally ruined.

But do not be afraid, I will not destroy you and your family. Make yourself a large Ark with many rooms in it. Apply a layer of pitch inside and outside the Ark, so that it is well protected from water. Store the Ark with all the provisions you may need. You shall take refuge in the Ark with your family. Also, take in with you a pair each of all living creatures - one male and one female."

Noah trusted God, and though the task entrusted to him was enormous, he set to work with his family.

Noah and his sons worked very hard to construct the Ark: soon, there was much sawing, hammering, and pounding going on outside his house.

Noah also preached the teachings of God to the people around him. "The Lord has said that he will send a flood, and destroy the earth and all the creatures. If you pray to the Lord, then you shall be saved."

But no one believed Noah. Instead, they jeered at him and his sons: "Look at these mad people. They think that it is going to rain! Who ever heard of water falling from the heavens? And imagine building a boat here! Miles from the sea! Ha! Ha!"

However, Noah and his sons didn't pay heed to their neighbors' unkind words, and kept working.

After one hundred and twenty years of labor, Noah and his sons completed their work. Next, provisions such as fruits, grains, hay, leaves, etc. were stored in the Ark. Then, with his family and the animals and birds that God specified, Noah went into the Ark.

Seven days after the last animal had stepped into the Ark, it began to rain. For forty days and forty nights, it rained continuously. As the water increased, it lifted the Ark high above the surface of the earth. The rains continued and the water kept on rising till the fields, valleys, hills, and mountains were completely drowned! But, the Ark kept on floating on the surface of the water. Every living thing perished; only Noah and those with him in the Ark were saved.

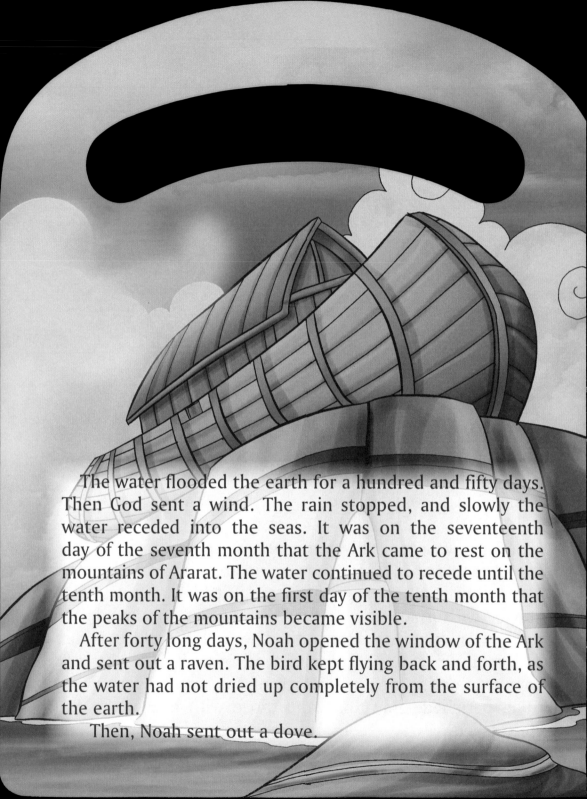

The water flooded the earth for a hundred and fifty days. Then God sent a wind. The rain stopped, and slowly the water receded into the seas. It was on the seventeenth day of the seventh month that the Ark came to rest on the mountains of Ararat. The water continued to recede until the tenth month. It was on the first day of the tenth month that the peaks of the mountains became visible.

After forty long days, Noah opened the window of the Ark and sent out a raven. The bird kept flying back and forth, as the water had not dried up completely from the surface of the earth.

Then, Noah sent out a dove.

But the dove also could not find any dry surface to place its feet, so, it returned to Noah in the Ark.

After seven days, Noah sent the dove out for the second time. This time, the dove returned with a freshly plucked olive leaf in its beak!

At once, Noah understood that the water had withdrawn from the earth. He waited for seven more days and sent the dove out again.

This time, it didn't return.

Cautiously, Noah removed the covering of the Ark and saw that the ground was dry.

At this time, God commanded Noah, "Come out of the Ark; you, your family, and all the creatures that are with you."

Following God's command, Noah and the other creatures came out of the Ark, on to a fresh new earth.

After stepping on the newly built earth, Noah created an altar for God, and made offerings on it.

God was pleased and made a covenant with Noah: "Never again will I curse the earth because of man. Never again shall I eliminate all the living creatures from the earth."

Then God blessed Noah, saying, "Be fruitful, and increase the number of your descendants who will fill the earth."